keeping MARRIAGES healthy

D1455937

by David and Teresa Ferguson

RVA is a global alliance empowering people to experience and reproduce great relationships. We offer a variety of resources and workshops to help every dimension of your relationships flourish.

Keeping Marriages Healthy
by David and Teresa Ferguson

For more information contact: Relational Values Alliance

2511 S. Lakeline Blvd., Cedar Park, TX 78613

ISBN 9798533877398

TABLE OF CONTENTS

keeping MARRIAGES *healthy*

- A practical help to make good marriages better!
- A timely preparation for an upcoming marriage!
- Hope and healing for troubled relationships!

Intimacy in Marriage

Intimacy—What is it?

What does the word mean to you?

In *Keeping Marriages Healthy*, we define intimacy as: *closeness, exclusiveness, freedom to share all of yourself with another person, both giving and receiving in your relationship, as well as deeply knowing one another so you're not alone.*

In order for intimacy to flourish, three things are necessary. First, there needs to be a desire to know and to be known. Secondly, there must be the willingness to be vulnerable and allow someone to know us. This second element cannot happen without a third—a motivation of care which leads to trust. We only make ourselves vulnerable if we are sure that the person who seeks to know us, cares for us and will not harm us.

Intimacy, therefore, means to know someone deeply and to be known by them—to be able to disclose innermost thoughts and feelings to someone who in turn chooses to reveal themselves to you. It means to be caringly involved with one another, choosing to affirm and build up rather than criticizing. In marriage there are two complex individuals often with very different personalities. Marriage gives us the opportunity to lovingly and deeply know each other in a special, intimate way. When this is achieved, only then will we be living within marriage as it was meant to be.

Life Events May Challenge Intimacy

Marriages typically pass through predictable stages initiated by certain life events:

- Early days together
- Settling into married life together
- First baby or struggling with infertility
- Employment/unemployment pressures
- Growing children
- Teenage pressures
- Children leaving home
- Responsibility for aging parents
- Retirement from employment

The marriage relationship has been created for specific purposes that we will explore together. Imagine the possibility that marriage was intended to be a source of great blessing in your journey together emotionally, spiritually, and physically.

During each of these stages, relationships can develop and mature as new challenges are faced. Sometimes external pressures or family tensions cause strain on the marriage, and previously enjoyed intimacy is lost. The arrival of a baby, the difficulties of making time for one another in the midst of both having demanding and challenging careers, time spent away from home on business trips, teenage years, extended family, and aging parents all create demands on time and emotions. It can become easy for a couple to drift apart, reacting to the most current pressing demand upon them, resulting in their own relationship receiving little attention. Too often couples reach the time of "the empty nest," when the children have grown up and left home, to find that they have few shared interests. The friendship in their relationship is lacking. In fact, the thought of the retirement years and spending even more time together is viewed with dread. Marriages reaching that stage have not collapsed overnight. The erosion has been gradual and often unnoticeable. The *Keeping Marriages Healthy* course is designed to equip us to maintain and even deepen our intimacy at every stage and through every challenge of life.

We will learn how to communicate love and affirmation on a regular basis, to deposit strength, and build closeness into our marriage relationship.

Finding opportunities to tell each other that you love one another will increase closeness, whatever your current stage or situation.

Consider turning to each other now and saying something like, "I'm glad you are/are going to be my husband/wife, and I'm looking forward to learning how to better love you."

Assess Your Relationship—Where are we?

We invite you to reflect upon your intimacy in each of these three dimensions.

- What does it mean to be a friend to each other?
- What would your spiritual or faith journey together involve?
- What does it mean to be physically intimate with my marriage partner?

Take a few minutes now to reflect on your relationship.

On the following page, indicate your perception of the degree of intimacy in each dimension. Place a mark on the scales to signify your view of your marriage health. Work individually on this. You will be sharing your thoughts later with each other.

Take this assessment and share with each other when prompted by the presenters.

1. The emotional or friendship dimension of our relationship is:

Lacking in Intimacy   Very Intimate

● ● ● ● ● ● ● ● ● ● ● ● ● ● ● ● ● ●

What aspect of being a friend to your spouse would you most like to see changed or improved in your relationship?

_____

_____

_____

2. Our spiritual beliefs and values are:

Lacking in Intimacy   Very Intimate

● ● ● ● ● ● ● ● ● ● ● ● ● ● ● ● ● ●

What beliefs or life values would you like to share more in together?

_____

_____

_____

3. The physical dimension of our relationship is:

Lacking in Intimacy   Very Intimate

● ● ● ● ● ● ● ● ● ● ● ● ● ● ● ● ● ●

What aspect of your physical closeness would you most like to see changed or improved in your relationship?

_____

_____

_____

Sharing Truth in Love

Reflect on the three dimensions of marriage intimacy noted on the previous page and finish the following sentences:

It would really mean a lot to me if we could...

_____

_____

I would look forward to us having more...

_____

_____

I think it would be great for us to...

_____

_____

Be sure to continue this skill of sharing the truth in love.

It is one of the best ways to share what you need with your partner.

Say words that are positive and hope-filled in a loving tone of voice. Use the pronouns "we" and "us."

Increasing Emotional Intimacy: Practical Ideas

Friendship takes time—You can't get close to someone who isn't there. When was your last fun time together without family or friends? What is the next thing you are looking forward to doing together to relax and enjoy being together?

Common interests—Spend time together sharing an interest. Prioritize each other's interests and know what each finds important or enjoyable. What would you look forward to doing together?

Feelings—When you talk, express how you feel. Share anxieties, hurts, and joys. This can be a challenge for many, but being able to share how you really feel with another will bring closeness.

Dream together—Set aside regular time for each of you to share goals about the future—your marriage, family, career, friends, finances, etc.

Think about a positive memory or celebration from your growing up years—a pleasant occasion when you felt loved, cared for, or special (e.g., a birthday, family trip, favorite holiday experience, receiving a much wanted pet, taking part in a school play, a sporting achievement, an activity shared with a friend, working alongside a parent).

Share that positive memory now with your partner.

As your partner shares with you, identify what feelings you have for him/her (e.g., happy, glad, joyful, excited).

Express those feelings to your partner. "I'm glad that happened; I'm excited for you; that sounds great."

Now swap roles.

What did it feel like to celebrate together?

Responding with joy about something good is an example of increasing care for each other. Sharing the good memory involves disclosing something about ourselves to each other. This exchange is an example of what's involved in knowing and caring for each other more deeply.

What Do We Really Need From Each Other?

keeping MARRIAGES healthy

More people are alive today than have ever lived in all of history combined. Yet in the bewildering complexities and pressures of modern life, we can often feel alone. Although living under the same roof and sharing the same bed, a husband and wife can still live separate lives with a distance growing between them. The demands of work, family, finances, and even friends can put an added strain on the marriage relationship.

In the healthiest marriages, couples work hard to address any aspect of distance, isolation, or aloneness that may come between them. After all, the hope of marriage is to truly know and be known by another person. Marriage can provide a consistent best friend for life's celebrations and sorrows. It can be a great provision so that we're not alone!

Can you think of a particular time when you felt alone (isolated, disconnected, like no one knew you or cared for you) and your partner was able to take away your sense of aloneness?

I remember feeling alone when...

_____

and my partner helped me by...

_____

The positive outcome of this was...

_____

One definition of intimacy, therefore, is the mutual removing of aloneness. This operates on many different levels (e.g., intellectually, emotionally, and physically). To experience intimacy within marriage there needs to be both giving and receiving. Nothing hinders love more than being taken for granted or ignored. This often brings only resentment and emotional withdrawal. If not resolved, it can often lead to marital conflict, emotional separation, and other painful outcomes. As painful as it may be, couples must acknowledge when they have been growing apart and determine to bridge the gap.

A critical way in which we become and remain close is through meeting each other's relational needs. Marriage is the primary adult relationship through which there is giving and receiving to meet emotional/relational needs. When needs are met, we feel close and aloneness is removed.

Needs Met and Unmet

Among our several physical needs are those for food and sleep. Depending upon how much sleep we have had, we either feel rested or irritable. If we have sufficient food, we feel satisfied, and if insufficient, we become weak.

In a similar way, when our relational needs are met, we experience fulfillment, feel loved, and sense closeness. If relational needs are unmet, we are frustrated and feel irritated, angry, and hurt. This is when we can begin to grow apart.

On a relational level, if one partner in the marriage hasn't received needed attention, affection, or appreciation, they may become vulnerable to moodiness, rejection, and retaliation or become uncommunicative and turn inward. It is also possible for that person to look elsewhere for those emotional needs to be met (e.g., friends, work, and children).

Our relational needs cannot be met if our partner is unaware of them. If we're unwilling or feel inadequate about how to share our needs in a healthy way, it will be difficult for our spouse to meet our needs. This is one reason why it is imperative to practice sharing the truth in love as mentioned in the previous chapter. Conflict may also arise if we are not careful to listen to and observe our partner's needs or come to know them deeply. Unmet needs are never easy to live with.

Needs do not go away simply by ignoring, suppressing, or denying them. We will never grow out of our neediness. We have the same need for attention and security when we are eight days old or 80 years of age. Just as a child thrives when receiving affection, attention, and affirmation, so our lives are more fulfilled when we continue to receive these things.

See the *Pain and Potential Model* on page 43 for a look at how needs unmet can lead to painful outcomes.

On the following page, you will find a list of the ten most common relational needs. In healthy marriages, couples not only become familiar with the vocabulary of these needs, they also spend time getting to know each person's most important needs and then making an intentional effort to give to one another in these ways.

You can find videos and digital growth plans that illustrate each need at www.relationalvalues.com or scan the QR code in the margin.

Ten Important Relational Needs

ACCEPTANCE   The need for acceptance is met when someone likes you even though you're different from them; they don't try to change you or fix you. Someone loves you even when you mess up; they give you a second chance. It sounds like this: I love you just the way you are! I'm glad I'm your friend even when you mess up.

AFFECTION   The need for affection is met by giving words, hugs, kisses, pats on the back, putting an arm around you, or sitting close to you. It sounds like this: You're really special! I love you.

APPRECIATION   The need for appreciation is met when someone recognizes your accomplishment or effort—especially noticing the things you have done and sharing their thanks. Appreciation is often given through certificates, medals, or trophies. It sounds like: You did a terrific job on the yard! Thank you for working hard and pitching in with the project. You played a great game last night!

APPROVAL   The need for approval is met when someone brags about you to others—especially for the kind of person you are, not just the things you do. Approval is given when someone affirms your character or says how proud they are to be in a relationship with you. It sounds like: I'm proud of you! You have a kind and generous heart. I'm so glad I get to be the parent of such an amazing kid!

ATTENTION   The need for attention is met when someone calls just to say they are thinking about you or want to spend time with you. It includes individual, undivided listening and an effort to get to know you and your needs. The need for attention is also met when someone attends your event, does the things you like to do, or enters your "world." It sounds like: Tell me about your day. How did your test go? What would you like to do this weekend?

COMFORT   The need for comfort is met by responding to a hurting person with words, feelings, and gentle touches. Giving comfort might include putting an arm around you when you're sad or sitting quietly and just "being there" during a difficult time. It might even include crying with you. It sounds like: I'm sad for you. I know you are really disappointed. I feel compassion for you and what you're going through.

ENCOURAGEMENT   The need for encouragement involves cheering someone on towards a goal. Giving encouragement includes making a phone call to inspire you on your big day, giving a note expressing belief in you, or sending a text that says, "You can do it!" It sounds like: I know you can make it! Don't give up; keep at it. I believe in you. You've got this!

RESPECT   The need for respect is met by treating one another as important and honoring one another with words and actions. It means giving the freedom to do the job your way and listening without interrupting. Respect includes checking with you before making plans that affect you, using an appropriate tone of voice, and apologizing when I've done something to hurt you. It sounds like: I'd like to hear your ideas. What do you prefer? I was wrong. Will you forgive me?

SECURITY   The need for security is met when there is safety and trust; there are no threats and no aspects of harm for you. Meeting the need for security means that someone provides for your needs, doesn't lose their temper with you, is dependable, and keeps their promises. It sounds like: I'm here for you. We're going to work this out. I'm going to keep my promise to you.

SUPPORT   The need for support is met by coming alongside you and providing gentle, appropriate help with a problem or struggle. It includes helping you with a big project, teaching you how, or doing hard things together. It sounds like: I'll be glad to help you. Just let me know. Would you like to try the first step together?

Relational Needs Assessment

Everyone needs all ten of these relational needs in some measure, however there will be two or three that often seem to matter most. Read through the definitions below. First, mark the three needs you consider most important for you to receive right now. Next, mark the three needs you think your partner would consider most important to receive.

Myself	Intimacy Needs	Partner
☐	**Acceptance:** Receiving another person unconditionally, when their behavior has been imperfect; continuing to love another in spite of differences or failures	☐
☐	**Affection:** Expressing care and closeness through physical touch; saying, "I love you."	☐
☐	**Appreciation**: Expressing thanks, praise, or commendation; recognizing accomplishment or effort particularly for what someone does	☐
☐	**Approval**: Building up or affirming another particularly for who they are; affirming the fact of and the importance of a relationship	☐
☐	**Attention**: Entering another's world; conveying appropriate interest, concern, and taking thought of another	☐
☐	**Comfort**: Responding to a hurting person with words, feelings, and touch; to hurt with and for another's grief or pain	☐
☐	**Encouragement**: Urging another to persist and persevere toward a goal; stimulating toward love and good deeds, particularly when someone is weary	☐
☐	**Respect**: Valuing and regarding one another highly; treating one another as important; honoring one another	☐
☐	**Security**: Ensuring harmony in relationships even as conflicts are resolved, deepening trust, expressing vulnerability, and providing freedom from fear or threat of harm	☐
☐	**Support**: Coming alongside and gently helping with a problem or struggle; providing appropriate assistance	☐

Now compare lists and make a note of the three needs you have chosen, alongside those your partner has chosen.

Your Needs	Partner's Needs
1. _____	1. _____
2. _____	2. _____
3. _____	3. _____

Have a conversation with your partner where you each share your top three relational needs.

Next, compare your lists. Discuss how many needs are the same or different. Using the guidelines below, discuss what this might mean for your relationship.

As you compare lists notice how many of your needs are the same.

☐ 0 the same

☐ 1 the same

☐ 2 the same

☐ 3 the same

What happens if the two lists have only one or even none the same?

First, be reassured that this is quite likely to be the case. We are more likely to be married to someone whose top needs are different from our own. What can happen, however, is a tendency to give to our partner the things we would actually like to receive ourselves. For example: One partner who has a top need for affection may not understand why the other seems ungrateful for all the abundant affection being offered. When in fact, demonstrations of respect might be the primary way this person feels loved.

What about those whose two lists are very similar?

Even though you and your partner may have similar needs, how you would like them met may be very different. Giving each other additional insight into how to best meet a need will be helpful.

For example: *"I really enjoy being greeted at the door when I come in from work. This shows me your* **affection**.*" Or "I feel really cared for when you say the words, 'I love you.' This is how to best show me* **affection**.*"*

For example: *"Going for a short walk together in the evening when we can talk about our day means a lot to me. That's what* **attention** *looks like for me." Or "You can meet my need for* **attention** *by giving me your undivided focus. I feel really loved when we talk without the distraction of TV or phones."*

Giving to each other in ways that makes each feel loved and cared for will be very important for building happiness and fulfillment in your marriage.

Turn to one another and say something like...

I really feel loved by you when...

_____

_____

and I think that might be related to my need for...

_____

_____

For example: "when you call me to tell me what time you will be home...my need for security" or "you ask me first before making any arrangements to play sports with your friends...my need for respect" or "you kiss me goodbye in the morning...my need for affection" or "you take time to listen to me when I'm down...my need for comfort."

This is **not** an opportunity to say, *"I wish you would...,"* rather to encourage your marriage partner in something they are already doing.

You will want to make a note of the ways in which your marriage partner has expressed feeling loved and cared for by you. You'll want to repeat these demonstrations of love again!

_____

_____

_____

The exercise **Special to Receive**, on the next page, can help you discover which demonstrations of love are meaningful for you and your partner. Mark the items listed that really appeal to you.

Ask your partner what he/she would most like to receive and mark those down. Take the opportunity in the next few weeks to give to each other from this list. The items chosen will also give insight into your partner's top needs.

A list like this is very limited, so you might like to take time to talk about what you would like added!

Choose four items and mark them in the ***Myself*** column.

Partner   Myself

☐   Holding hands   ☐

☐   Going for a walk   ☐

☐   An unexpected hug   ☐

☐   Finding a love note   ☐

☐   Receiving a surprise gift   ☐

☐   Being served a favorite meal   ☐

☐   Being told "I love you"   ☐

☐   Helping with the children   ☐

☐   Being approached sexually   ☐

☐   Seeing the house in order   ☐

☐   Helping with things around the house   ☐

☐   Receiving compliments on my looks   ☐

☐   Taking a shower together   ☐

☐   A surprise night out   ☐

☐   Getting a back massage   ☐

☐   Having dinner together   ☐

☐   Having a quiet conversation   ☐

Any additional items:

_____

_____

We are "hard-wired" to connect, but we don't always know how. That's why we provide resources for anyone who wants to strengthen their relationship skills.

Relational Needs Assessment

This Relational Needs Assessment will enable you to go a step further in identifying your actual top relational needs and gain better understanding of what it looks like to have your needs met and meet the needs of your partner.

This assessment can be found in the appendix of this book on page 37. You can also find this assessment on our website at www.relationalvalues.com/relational-needs or by simply scanning the QR code below.

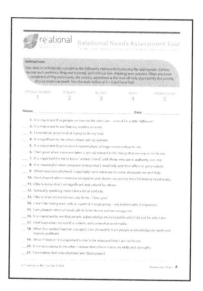

Relational Health

In this resource, you'll learn about the most important intimacy needs and how they can be met. You'll learn what it sounds like to meet the need of attention, what it looks like to show support, and how impacting it can be when we meet the need of comfort. Discover the rich potential of relationships when we meet these same needs in the lives of one another.

To purchase this workbook, go to www.relationalvalues.com/shop or scan the QR code below.

What is Filling Your Emotional Cup? Part 1

When our relational needs are met, we experience intimacy; when our needs are unmet, we experience hurt and loss. We might express this truth as an intimacy *equation*:

Intimacy Needs—MET = Feeling special, loved, and cared for

But there is another all–important intimacy equation:

Intimacy Needs—UNMET = Feeling unimportant, unloved, uncared for, and hurt

Any marriage is going to experience misunderstandings, disappointments, let-downs, hurts, and rejections. The actions/inactions that produce these feelings are most often unintentional, but they still cause us pain. No one can meet their marriage partner's needs perfectly because there are no perfect people. Hurt is inevitable. The question then is, *"What are we doing with the hurt we all experience?"*

How do we deal with emotional pain?

The primary part of our brain that's in charge of emotion is called the amygdala. This area of our brain can be compared to a small cup that contains all of our emotions. If our emotional cup is filled with positive emotions because our needs are met, then our cup will overflow with positive things like love, joy, and peace. However, if negative feelings fill our emotional cup, they can crowd out positive emotions. We are left experiencing such things as hurt, bitterness, anger, guilt, fear, anxiety, and stress.

keeping MARRIAGES healthy

Hurt

The initial emotional response to unmet needs is hurt, sadness, and disappointment. We may not consciously feel the pain, but it is there.

Anger

When we are hurt, our pain is often masked by anger. Our hurt feelings leave us saddened and vulnerable to more pain, so in order to defend ourselves, we often turn outward and become angry at others.

Recognizing that underneath anger is hurt gives us understanding that if we show care for the hurt, then the anger will be softened.

Anger can be expressed in different ways. It can look like impatience, a quick temper, depression, jealousy, suspicion, sarcasm, or emotional distance.

Fear

Our unmet need can produce not only hurt and anger but also fear. If we are hurt, we not only feel that pain, but we also fear more hurt in the future. If something we have done is criticized and ridiculed, we feel the pain deeply now, but we also fear future failures as well.

Fear can also take several forms. One response to fear is withdrawal. A person might avoid situations that bring further hurt. Another response can be to become controlling, thinking that being in charge will minimize future pain. Fear can also result in perfectionism, believing that a perfect performance will reduce the chance of hurt. Trying to numb our fear and anxiety can lead us to addiction to alcohol, drugs, or even "good" things like work!

Guilt and Shame/Condemnation

Hurt and anger can also lead to guilt. Retaliation for hurt received may mean we, in turn, hurt others. We may attack and then feel guilt for the hurt we have caused. Guilt is associated with a specific act.

Shame and condemnation feel similar to guilt; however, they are not the same. Condemnation causes us to feel that everything is our fault. It attacks our self-worth and makes us feel both like a failure and responsible for the hurt we have received. Shame and condemnation are not related to specific actions like true guilt; therefore, they can't be confessed and forgiven in the same way. Guilt comes when we have done something wrong. Shame and condemnation say that there is something fundamentally wrong with who we are; our worth and value is in question.

THE EMOTIONAL CUP

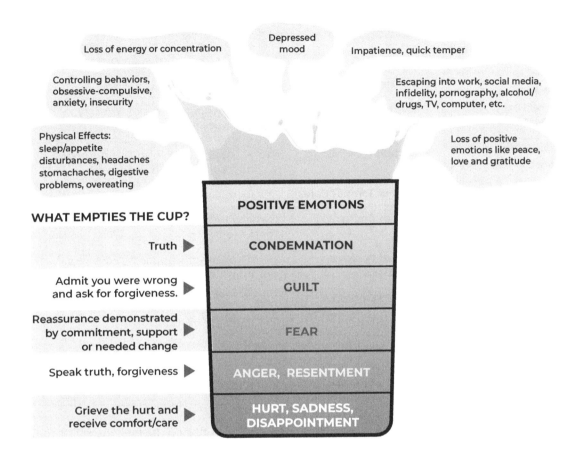

Loss of energy or concentration

Depressed mood

Impatience, quick temper

Controlling behaviors, obsessive-compulsive, anxiety, insecurity

Escaping into work, social media, infidelity, pornography, alcohol/drugs, TV, computer, etc.

Physical Effects: sleep/appetite disturbances, headaches stomachaches, digestive problems, overeating

Loss of positive emotions like peace, love and gratitude

WHAT EMPTIES THE CUP?

Antidote	Emotion
	POSITIVE EMOTIONS
Truth ▶	CONDEMNATION
Admit you were wrong and ask for forgiveness. ▶	GUILT
Reassurance demonstrated by commitment, support or needed change ▶	FEAR
Speak truth, forgiveness ▶	ANGER, RESENTMENT
Grieve the hurt and receive comfort/care ▶	HURT, SADNESS, DISAPPOINTMENT

UNMET RELATIONAL NEEDS OFTEN BRING ONE OR MORE OF THESE PAINFUL EMOTIONS. THIS DECREASES OUR CAPACITY FOR POSITIVE EMOTION AND OFTEN RESULTS IN UNHEALTHY SYMPTOMS.

THE GOOD NEWS: WHEN WE APPLY THE RIGHT ANTIDOTE, OUR EMOTIONAL CUP CAN BE EMPTIED!

Have a conversation with your spouse. What symptoms might be true when your emotional cup is full?

Make this an honest and sincere conversation.

Remember: This is not a time to blame or accuse your partner. Simply own up to your own symptoms with courage and vulnerability.

Symptoms of Emotional Cup Overflow

Does your behavior show that your cup is filled with painful emotions?

Physical Effects	Feeling tired all the time, unable to sleep, overeating/not eating/comfort eating, headaches, or digestive problems
Controlling Behaviors	Obsessive–compulsive, anxiety, insecurity
Depressed Mood	Irrational fears, depression, anxiety, worrying unnecessarily
Escaping Behaviors	Work, social media, infidelity, pornography, alcohol/drugs, TV, computer, etc.
Lack of Temper Control	Impatient, easily angered or irritated
Loss of Energy	Inability to concentrate, inability to feel motivated
Loss of Positive Emotions	No fun any more, apparent coldness, unromantic, unable to give or receive love

Other symptoms:

_____

_____

_____

Some of the symptoms you might see when my emotional cup is full would be: _____.

Next, let's consider our emotional cups and the feelings which may have accumulated, especially hurt.

Some of the pain has come from our marriage, but some of the pain was already there—prior to or apart from our marriage. We begin by addressing how to care for the hurt and sadness from sources other than our marriage. Later, we will address how our marriage hurts can be healed.

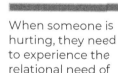

When someone is hurting, they need to experience the relational need of comfort.

When your partner is hurting (and you haven't been a part of causing that hurt), they need your comfort.

Comfort means:

- Sharing words that show care and compassion
- Telling how my heart is impacted because of what they have experienced
- Sharing emotion with emotion

When your spouse is hurting, they need you to hurt with them!

The illustration on page 17, entitled *Developing Relational Skills of Emotional Responding*, illustrates what comfort **does** and **does not** look like and sound like.

UNPRODUCTIVE RESPONSES

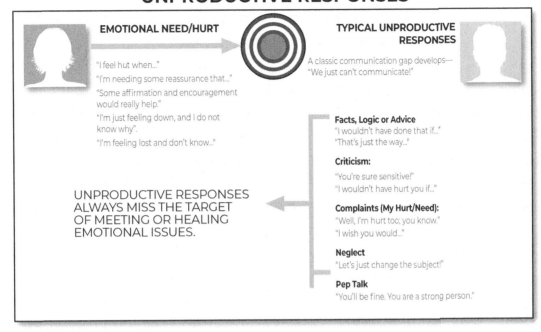

EMOTIONAL NEED/HURT

"I feel hurt when..."

"I'm needing some reassurance that..."

"Some affirmation and encouragement would really help."

"I'm just feeling down, and I do not know why".

"I'm feeling lost and don't know..."

UNPRODUCTIVE RESPONSES ALWAYS MISS THE TARGET OF MEETING OR HEALING EMOTIONAL ISSUES.

TYPICAL UNPRODUCTIVE RESPONSES

A classic communication gap develops—"We just can't communicate!"

Facts, Logic or Advice
"I wouldn't have done that if..."
"That's just the way..."

Criticism:
"You're sure sensitive!"
"I wouldn't have hurt you if..."

Complaints (My Hurt/Need):
"Well, I'm hurt too; you know."
"I wish you would..."

Neglect
"Let's just change the subject!"

Pep Talk
"You'll be fine. You are a strong person."

EMOTIONAL RESPONDING

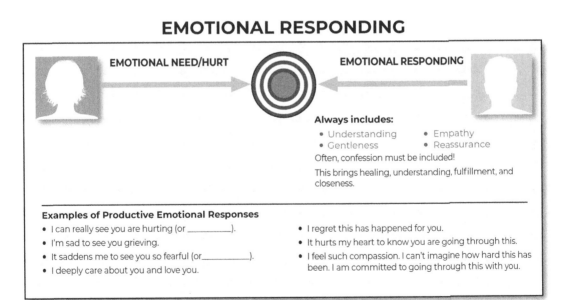

EMOTIONAL NEED/HURT

EMOTIONAL RESPONDING

Always includes:
- Understanding
- Empathy
- Gentleness
- Reassurance

Often, confession must be included!

This brings healing, understanding, fulfillment, and closeness.

Examples of Productive Emotional Responses
- I can really see you are hurting (or _____).
- I'm sad to see you grieving.
- It saddens me to see you so fearful (or_____).
- I deeply care about you and love you.
- I regret this has happened for you.
- It hurts my heart to know you are going through this.
- I feel such compassion. I can't imagine how hard this has been. I am committed to going through this with you.

Comforting Your Spouse

Comfort for a Childhood Memory

Think about a painful memory perhaps from childhood...a memory of a time you felt lonely, unloved, misunderstood, rejected, or afraid. (This time should **not** be related to your partner.)

Recall an embarrassing moment, a time when failure was experienced such as not getting a part in a school play or sport team, a family tragedy experienced, being called names, witnessing something traumatic or frightening.

1. Tell your partner about your painful memory:

I remember when...

_____

_____

_____

Here are some video clips to remind you what comfort is and is not.

and I felt...

_____

_____

SCAN ME

SCAN ME

2. Share words of comfort. What feelings do you have FOR your partner as you hear this painful memory expressed to you? (You may find yourself feeling anger towards the person who caused this hurt. Concentrate instead on the feelings for your husband/wife and how they experienced this pain.)

Express your feelings of sadness and sorrow in comforting words such as:

I feel a lot of compassion for you because...I feel sad, knowing that you...

I want you to know that I care about...I'm committed to go through this with you. I hurt for you. I'd like to understand your pain. It hurts my heart to know that...because I love you.

3. Now swap roles.

Perhaps you heard something you have never heard before. You may have been familiar with the event but heard it in a different way.

Recalling the memory and being comforted did nothing to change the circumstances, but it will give the opportunity to remove your aloneness in the pain. What did it feel like to have your partner feel with you and for you in your pain?

What Is Filling Your Emotional Cup? Part 2

In every marriage, conflict, difficulty, and pain are inevitable. In even the best of marriages, both husbands and wives make mistakes, forget things, overlook needs, get too busy, or even take each other for granted. There really is no such thing as a perfect marriage. Why? Because, it is a relationship between two imperfect people.

The difficulties may be loud and angry, or they may be quiet and even somewhat hidden, but the question is not, "Do we hurt each other?" Rather, the question is, "When, how, and how much do we hurt each other, and how do we go about healing this hurt?"

How do I help heal the hurts I have caused my marriage partner?

The first step in breaking the pain cycle is to identify the hurts you have caused. Next it's important to confess these faults to your marriage partner. Admit they were wrong. Don't rationalize or blame anyone else. Don't analyze the situation and explain away your responsibility. Try to understand the hurt from your partner's point of view. Your partner may be hurting about something that makes no sense from your perspective. If he/she is feeling hurt, you need to express your care. Caring for your partner means addressing the hurt with compassion and apology.

Understanding and Compassion for a Marital Hurt

Words need to be spoken humbly and sincerely, without excuses, rationalizing, explanations, minimizing of the other's hurt, or blaming. Unintentional hurt still hurts!

The tone of voice needs to communicate, "I really care about you and your feelings, and it saddens me that I have hurt you." This helps bring about healing of the pain.

For example: I am now aware how my lack of sensitivity has hurt you. When I don't let you know I will be late coming home, you feel disrespected and insecure. I have done this many times. I have been very insensitive to your feelings. You shouldn't have to worry about where I am and if I'm all right. I was wrong to have put you through this. My insensitivity and lack of dependability hurts you. I see how it impacts you. Will you forgive me?

Keeping a healthy marriage will require becoming skilled at apologizing for the ways in which I have hurt my partner. Hurting one another is inevitable. Apologizing is a choice!

Guidelines for an Effective Confession

- Be specific. A good confession of guilt is never general.
- Admit wrong without explaining/rationalizing.
- Show understanding of the other person's feelings.
- Specifically ask for forgiveness.

Couple Sharing Time

Think of a recent, specific incident when you disappointed or hurt your spouse. Perhaps you were selfish, spoke harshly, or failed to give encouragement. This recent wrong may not have been as hurtful as other incidents from the past, but this is a good opportunity to confess and forgive each other using a recent example. Go through all the stages needed for forgiveness to be offered and received. (See page 62 for possible ways we can hurt our partner.)

I was wrong when...

_____

_____.

I know you must have felt...

_____

_____.

because...

_____

_____.

Will you forgive me?

- Finally, verbalize reassurance and care for one another.
- Focus on the new memory of forgiveness.

Refer to pages 59–62 for additional help in navigating the confession and forgiveness process. You'll find these tools to be extremely helpful for conflict resolution.

A Great Resource to Continue to Grow in Emotional Wholeness

SCAN ME

This workbook presents a practical perspective on human emotions. It discusses the primary, painful emotions (hurt, anger, fear, guilt, condemnation, and stress) of your Emotional Cup and then leads you through antidotes for how to resolve those emotions. This resource helps the reader address painful emotions through the context of loving relationships with other people.

To purchase this workbook, go to www.relationalvalues.com/shop or scan the QR code in the margin of this page.

The Family Tree

One of the most significant ways we develop intimacy is by leaving behind certain things from our family of origin. We can only experience true closeness with our spouse when we have looked back at our childhood and left those things that hinder closeness. Most of us need to recognize that we are still holding on to some things that need to be left behind.

Taking a Look Back

Many of us experience a resistance to looking back at our childhood. **Some feel that what is past is in the past. Why dredge it up?** The truth is: Past events can cause pain in the present and need to be addressed. Not only can looking back give us understanding about the present, we can also experience additional healing through the intimacy of sharing these experiences with our spouse.

Others may say, "My past isn't affecting me; therefore, I have no need to look back." Through this chapter, we will look at how we are all affected, both positively and negatively, by past events in our upbringing.

Another view can be that our past really doesn't matter any way. We've discovered that some individuals who have a great deal of pain from childhood need the safety of a caring relationship to see that their pain does matter and they are worth caring for.

Anxiety about dishonoring parents, or criticizing a beloved parent who has now died, can also cause reluctance to look back at our childhood. Again, the goal is not to blame, accuse, or criticize. We do need to understand, however, that we can only truly honor real people and real people are imperfect. Our relationship with parents and caregivers is just like our marriage relationship. There are/were unintentional hurts and inevitable mistakes. Imperfect parents choose methods of parenting that cause their much–loved children pain. Imperfect parents miss meeting needs for their kids. Perfect people do not exist and neither do perfect families.

The goal of looking back is not to focus primarily on what others did or did not do, but rather upon our disappointments, hurts, and losses. Being vulnerable with our spouse about times of sadness, disappointment, and hurt from childhood *(that we may have dealt with alone)* can give an opportunity for us to receive their comfort and care now.

For some of us, it is a huge journey to arrive at the point of saying, *"My father and/or my mother gave me everything they had to give. I did miss some important things, and that did hurt."*

Identifying Three Things that Need to Be Left

On the day of a couple's wedding there is much anticipation and excitement about the future. As the ceremony ends and they turn to face family and friends as a husband and wife, thoughts are directed to the new life they are starting together. That is perhaps not the time to be thinking about anything except what lies ahead. However, once the early days of married life begin, it soon becomes very clear that each person brings certain things into the relationship. Some of these things need to be left behind.

1. Beliefs/Expectations

Our personal set of beliefs includes the expectation we have of roles in marriage. How are we going to sort out our expectations of each other in this relationship? There may be the view that women do certain jobs around the house, and men do others (i.e., Who takes the trash out, locks up at night, drives the car on long journeys, helps the children with their homework, checks the oil in the car...) There are no right or wrong answers on these issues, but each of us may have strong views that are often related to our experiences in our childhood home.

In order for the relationship to reach greater intimacy, some of these views may need to be left behind, especially when the association is made between love being given and a particular role being fulfilled (i.e., a husband shows love by always taking out the trash; a wife shows love by cooking all the meals)!

How we view others (both within the family and outside) may be another set of beliefs that create a challenge to intimacy. One person may have grown up with the view, "Look after yourself because no one else will." Another may have experienced an, "Always be ready to help someone else," attitude in the their childhood home. We may not even realize other families don't share or practice the view we grew up with.

The thought processes we use to recognize and resolve the things that happen to us are another aspect of this. In a later session, we will look at thinking patterns that can damage healthy relationships. Most of the thinking that shapes our marriage was learned at home in childhood.

2. Behaviors

Patterns of behavior are also learned in childhood. How we do certain things, which we may suddenly find is not a part of our husband or wife's childhood family experiences, is an intrinsic part of family life. Behavior that worked in your childhood home may no longer be appropriate. Some of us want to swing completely the opposite way in our adult behavior because some of our experiences as a child were painful and sad, and we want to do things very differently as adults. We either seem to embrace what we saw in childhood or react against it. Perhaps a better way is recognizing that in marriage, greater closeness will result when we both determine how we want to handle things in our relationship.

Have this conversation (noted on page 24) with your spouse:

"I think I need to leave this belief or expectation behind..."

Watch this video to laugh at all the crazy things couples fight about. Be sure to laugh at yourselves too.

Sometimes, we find ourselves engaging in unproductive behaviors in marriage particularly when honest, vulnerable communication has failed. Instead of needs being vulnerably expressed, attempts might be made to have needs met by game playing. For example, the "Nothing is wrong" game is one of the unproductive behaviors that needs to be left behind. In this game, one person denies anything is wrong, but their tone of voice and facial and body expression makes it clear the opposite is true. If that denial is maintained, the other partner may inquire about what is really the matter until their patience dissipates. The need still isn't met and now there is anger, frustration, and feelings of exclusion and neglect for both partners. (The need for attention in this game has not been given freely and lovingly, and so it isn't satisfying!) However unsatisfactory, this game is played surprisingly often. The solution to this game is to practice expressing needs truthfully.

One of the behaviors that is also crucial to our marriage journey is to explore the ways conflict was handled when we were growing up. One person might say, "I saw a lot of conflict growing up. It was loud, and it was obvious." Another person might say, "I don't think I saw any conflict, but we had a lot of times when it was very quiet and cold at home." Some families seem to engage in every opportunity for a fight while others avoid conflict at all costs. Each of us needs to explore how we saw conflict in our formative years.

Those who are parents might ask how our children would answer the question, "How did you see conflict handled while you were growing up?" A positive response would be the child who is able to say, "I often saw my father apologizing to my mother and heard her forgiving him. I also saw my mother apologizing to my father and heard him forgive her." That is a great way for conflict to be resolved.

Another behavior that may need to be left behind concerns the way in which affection was given and received in our homes. Some homes are places where affection is offered often through hugs and cuddles and is regularly verbalized. Other families rarely show affection through words or actions. Some families seem to find difficulty either receiving or giving affection. Each of us needs to ask the question "What did affection look like when we were growing up?" Some of us painfully may have little recollection of receiving affection, either verbally or through appropriate touch. Some adults may even have tried taking affection from us inappropriately, at best, causing confusion or, at worst, deep hurt and pain.

3. Emotions

While most of us would look at our wedding day as a new start, a fresh beginning, we quickly find that we both come into the marriage relationship with certain emotional baggage. Understanding your spouse better and particularly all that they bring into this relationship from the past will give you some incredible ways to love them in the present.

Unresolved anger, fears, guilt, and shame from childhood and unhealed hurt from unmet needs can also all be brought into those early months and years of marriage. These unresolved emotions can affect the quality of marriage because it affects our thinking, our reactions, and our feelings about family life.

Have this conversation (noted on page 24) with your spouse:

"I think I need to leave this behavior behind..."

What may need to be left behind?

In order to have a healthy marriage, we need to unpack the unhelpful baggage from our past, especially from our childhood. When we identify what we brought into our marriage, are grateful for what is good and meaningful, and then leave behind what is not good, true, or helpful our marriage thrives.

Share with one another the things that need to be left behind from your family of origin:

1. Beliefs/Expectations

I think I will need to leave this belief or expectation behind...

_____

_____

_____

_____

_____

2. Certain Behaviors

I think I might need to leave this behavior behind...

_____

_____

_____

_____

3. Certain Painful Emotions

Hurts from childhood that need to be left behind include...

_____

_____

I will choose to share that hurt with my spouse and receive comfort...

_____

_____

Intimacy Needs in Childhood

Unmet needs in childhood could still be influencing your relationships as an adult unless these needs are understood and the losses faced. It is helpful to assess the degree to which relational needs were met or not met by your parents/guardians in childhood.

Look at the Relational Needs listed below and ask...

1. "How did my mother consistently meet this need?" If you can recall specific ways in which she met this need, put a half circle next to that need on the list (i.e., you may recall her telling you stories at bedtime which met your need for attention).

2. "How did your father consistently meet this need?" If you can recall specific times and ways your father met this need, put a half circle next to that need on the list (i.e., you may remember your dad giving you a hug when you had a problem at school, which met your need for comfort).

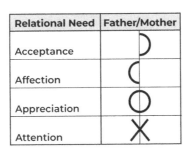

Relational Need	Father/Mother
Acceptance	☽
Affection	☾
Appreciation	○
Attention	✗

If only one person met a need, you will have a half–circle beside it. If both parents/guardians met the need, you will have a full circle.

Place an X beside any of the needs that are blank, indicating that those needs were not met consistently by either mother or father.

Relational Need	Father/Mother	
Acceptance		
Affection		
Appreciation		
Attention		
Approval		
Comfort		
Encouragement		
Respect		
Security		
Support		

After completing the assessment, celebrate needs met with your partner.

My need for _____ was

often met by _____,

and I am so grateful that_____

_____.

For those needs that were not sufficiently met in childhood, share the loss with your partner and receive comfort.

My need for _____ was

often not met by _____,

and I feel _____

_____

because _____

_____.

After each person has completed the assessment and reflected on their needs met and needs missed, share responses with one another. First, celebrate needs met with your partner.

Partner one shares:

My need for _____ was often met by _____ , and I am so grateful that_____

_____.

Celebrate with one another

Partner two responds with celebration:

I'm so glad you experienced that because...

It makes me happy to know that you...

Switch roles *so that each person shares needs that were met and both gives and receives celebration.*

Next, each person shares about the needs that were not sufficiently met in childhood. Share the loss with your partner and receive comfort.

Partner one shares:

My need for _____ was often not met by _____ , and I feel _____

because _____

_____.

Comfort one another

Partner two responds with comfort:

I feel sad knowing that you missed that need because...

I'm so sorry you went through that. It must have really hurt.

I feel a lot of compassion for you because...and I love you.

Switch roles *so that each person shares needs that were missed and both gives and receives comfort.*

Make these moments of celebration and comfort a consistent part of your relationship. As additional insights about needs met and needs missed from childhood come to mind, continue these conversations. This is an important part of a healthy marriage!

Break Free from Unhealthy Thinking

One of the additional impacts from our growing up years relates to our thinking patterns. Our experiences during our growing up years can impact how we think about the world, how we approach it, and specifically, how we interact with our marriage partner.

Thinking Patterns

A thinking pattern is the habitual way our minds process what is happening to us and around us. Some of our thinking patterns are good and healthy, reflecting what is true. Some are not. Some of our thinking patterns may reflect significant distortions of truth, which hinder our ability to handle life and experience intimacy in our relationships. We may have seen certain ways of thinking modeled by parents, family members, or others in authority and need to ask whether those patterns reflect the truth.

In this chapter, we'll address six, common unhealthy thinking patterns and explore which ones we are prone to exhibit. Faulty and unhealthy thinking needs to be challenged and replaced with truth. Your spouse can be a perfect balance to any unhealthy thinking and a great help as you embrace more truthful thinking.

Unhealthy Thinking Questionnaire

Review the statements on the next page. Check the statements you agree with, first for yourself and then for your spouse. In other words, are the statements true for you? Do the statements seem true for your spouse? Leave the box blank if you disagree.

keeping **MARRIAGES** healthy

Unhealthy Thinking Questionnaire

Myself   Spouse

- ☐ 1. I see things very much as right or wrong. ☐
- ☐ 2. I tend to make mountains out of molehills. ☐
- ☐ 3. I often take things personally. ☐
- ☐ 4. Past disappointments seem to predict the future. ☐
- ☐ 5. What I am feeling is more important that the facts. ☐
- ☐ 6. I often think people make too much of their problems. They should just get over it. ☐
- ☐ 7. There is a place for everything and everything in it's place. ☐
- ☐ 8. Many things seem to be a major issue. ☐
- ☐ 9. It's very important to sense others' approval. ☐
- ☐ 10. I just know things won't get any better. ☐
- ☐ 11. I can't really believe I'm loved unless I feel it. ☐
- ☐ 12. I can handle almost any problem that comes my way. I don't really need much support from anyone. ☐
- ☐ 13. Being perfect in what I undertake is essential to me. ☐
- ☐ 14. I seem to overreact to relatively small irritations. ☐
- ☐ 15. If someone in my family is upset, I must have been part of the reason. ☐
- ☐ 16. I tend to cross people off my list if they hurt or disappoint me. ☐
- ☐ 17. If I feel unloved, it must be because no one loves me. ☐
- ☐ 18. There's no reason to get so upset or so emotional. ☐

Now look over each of the statements that were true for you.

The chart below gives the statements that match the six unhealthy patterns. Find the items that you agreed with then identify/circle which thinking pattern(s) the statement represents.

Have a conversation with your spouse. Talk about your tendencies toward un-healthy thinking. Make this a fun, light-hearted conversation. Laugh at yourself and be open to your partner's feedback.

Polarizing

All is right or wrong.

1, 7, 13

Magnifying

All is a big deal.

2, 8, 14

Personalizing

All is an attack.

3, 9, 15

Generalizing

Past = Future

4, 10, 16

Emotional Reasoning

Feelings are facts.

5, 11, 17

Minimizing

All is a little deal.

6, 12, 18

The thinking pattern that you most identify with is the one selected the most often. Share your responses with your spouse.

According to this exercise, I have a tendency toward:

_____

_____

_____

_____

These unhealthy thinking patterns contribute to emotional pain. Everyone is prone to at least one of these patterns.

According to this exercise, my spouse seems to have a tendency toward:

_____

_____

_____

_____

HINT: Your marriage partner may have helpful insights about your thinking pattern(s). Their insights may even be more accurate than your own. Listen carefully and non-defensively to your partner's view.

How These Six Thought Patterns Might Be Displayed

A Comparison

John Smith has worked for a company for the past three years. He has just received notice that due to a recession, the company will be laying off 400 employees, and he's one of them. What kind of thinking might John have in response to this news?

If he "polarizes," he may respond:

"So that's the decision—layoffs. If they don't want me, then I certainly don't want them. That is the end of the line for this company!"

If he "magnifies," he may respond:

"This is the worst thing that could possibly happen! My life is over! I'm ruined. What am I going to do?"

If he "personalizes," he may respond:

"I knew my boss didn't like me. He's been waiting for a chance to get rid of me. What did I do wrong?"

If he "generalizes," he may respond:

"This was bound to happen sooner or later. This always seems to happen to me—I'll never keep a steady job."

If he "emotionally reasons," he may respond:

"I'm so angry about this. There is something else going on here. This isn't just about economic recession; it feels as though we're not getting the whole truth here."

If he "minimizes," he may respond:

"Well it's no big deal; these things happen. I don't want to talk about it. What's done is done—not much any of us can do about it."

Breaking Free

Recognizing which thinking patterns we struggle with and how they impact our marriage is important. One pattern may be obvious to us, but we may be unaware of additional patterns. Admitting to your marriage partner that you recognize a tendency to think in a certain way, asking for support in overcoming that unhealthy reaction, and seeing the truth is an excellent place to start. We have greater difficulty correcting these thinking patterns when we try to do it alone.

You may have recognized one predominate thinking pattern for yourself and another for your spouse. Sometimes the combination can create stresses. A minimizer and a magnifier living together can be very frustrating.

Pointing out the truth of a situation with gentleness and understanding may bring a change in thinking that a negative, critical, complaining approach will not achieve. Each spouse needs to recognize that overcoming unhealthy thinking may be a real struggle that will require support, understanding, and many loving conversations with your partner.

HINT: To learn more about unhealthy thinking patterns, check the appendix, pages 44–51.

Intimacy Becoming a Way of Life

keeping MARRIAGES healthy

In healthy marriages, couples take the time and are intentional about investing in their relationship. The strongest couples don't wait until their marriage is in trouble to invest; they work hard to make the habits of intimacy a way of life.

Simply put, one of the best ways to invest in your marriage is to consistently meet your partner's relational needs. A healthy marriage takes two people who focus on giving to one another. If you want a marriage that lasts a lifetime, find out your spouse's top relational needs and work hard to meet those needs in ways that are meaningful to them.

Another way to see this opportunity of relationship is this: In healthy marriages, couples stay at the top of the Pain and Potential Chart. The chart below describes the painful reality when we *miss* our partner's relational needs and the incredible potential that's available when we *meet* our partner's relational needs.

THE PAIN AND POTENTIAL OF RELATIONAL NEEDS

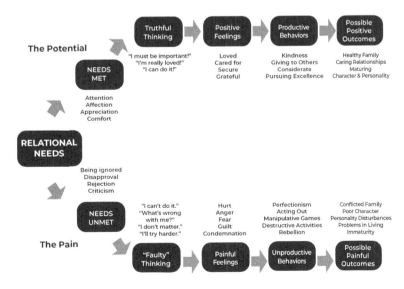

(View a larger version of this graphic on page 43)

Meet your partner's relational need, and it produces good things like positive thoughts, feelings, and behaviors. Months and years of meeting relational needs produces outcomes like intimacy, closeness, and health. Miss your partner's need, and it produces painful thoughts, feelings, and behaviors. Months and years of unmet needs produces painful outcomes like distance, coldness, conflict, and divorce.

Here's a practical way to meet a need for your partner. We encourage you to continue your *Keeping Marriages Healthy* journey by meeting one of your partner's relational needs such as the need for approval. This is one of the skills that will help the intimacy in your marriage last a lifetime.

Gratitude for Your Partner's Character

As you look at the following list of 30 character qualities, choose the ones that describe your partner (preferably three or more). Express your gratitude for those particular qualities in your partner. This will be most meaningful if you can also identify a time when you recall this quality being demonstrated and share that also.

For example: I am grateful for your **dependability**. *I saw that trait in you when...*

You make me smile when I see your _____. I especially notice that...

30 Character Qualities

ACCEPTANCE A ready willingness to receive others unconditionally

CAUTIOUSNESS Looking for appropriate and relevant guidance before making decisions; being observant of distracting or destructive situations and taking action to resist

COMPASSION Having empathy with the hurts of others and being ready to do anything possible to relieve another's pain

CONTENTMENT Enjoying present possessions rather than desiring new or additional ones; knowing that happiness and inner peace are not found in possessions or position

CREATIVITY Finding ways to overcome seemingly impossible obstacles; discovering practical applications for beliefs and values

DECISIVENESS Finalizing difficult decisions on the basis of values, principles, and beliefs, not just current circumstances

DEFERENCE Limiting your freedom in order not to offend the personal, strongly held preferences of others

DEPENDABILITY Learning to be true to a promise even when difficulties are faced in fulfilling that commitment

DILIGENCE Seeing every task as an important assignment and applying whatever energy and concentration is needed for accomplishment

DISCERNMENT Knowing what to look for in evaluating people, problems, and situations; seeing the future consequences of words and actions; sensitivity; saying the right words at the right time

ENDURANCE Maintaining commitment to a goal during times of pressure; recognizing and laying aside hindrances

FORGIVENESS Acknowledging personal failings and being willing to accept and forgive the mistakes of others

GENEROSITY Learning how to be a wise steward and readily giving a share of possessions, money, or time in the assistance and support of others

GENTLENESS Knowing what is appropriate to meet the emotional needs of others; learning to respond to needs with kindness and love

GRATEFULNESS Recognizing the benefits which others have provided; looking for appropriate ways to express genuine appreciation

HOSPITALITY Learning to provide an atmosphere which makes others feel well treated and accepted; readiness to share life with others

HUMILITY Recognizing an inability to accomplish anything single-handedly; valuing others for their contribution to a successful outcome

INITIATIVE Taking the lead in acting and assuming responsibility for the support and encouragement of others involved; giving first

LOYALTY Adopting personally the wishes and goals of those being served

MEEKNESS Demonstrating how to earn the right to be heard rather than demanding a hearing; a willingness to surrender rights for the well-being of others

PATIENCE An ability and willingness to suppress annoyance when confronted by delay or frustrations; accepting difficult situations but working through them patiently

PUNCTUALITY Showing esteem for other people and their time by not keeping them waiting

REVERENCE A feeling or attitude of deep respect; to give honor

SELF CONTROL Control or restraint of thoughts, words, and actions

SENSITIVITY	Being alert to the motives and difficulties of others; looking past the obvious; knowing how to give the right words at the right time
SINCERITY	Having motives that are transparent; having a genuine concern to benefit the lives of others
THOROUGHNESS	Paying careful attention to details important for success
TOLERANCE	Learning how to respond to the immaturity of others without accepting their standard of immaturity
TRUTHFULNESS	Gaining approval of others without misrepresenting the facts; facing the consequences of a mistake. Telling the whole truth
VIRTUE	Learning to build personal moral standards which will result in excellence and benefit the lives of others

As a final exercise in your *Keeping Marriages Healthy* journey we invite you to consider one of the ways that you might need to grow or change. In healthy marriages, each partner takes initiative and responsibility for how they can personally contribute to the health and intimacy of the relationship. Towards this goal, reflect on how you might finish the sentences below and then share them with your partner.

To keep our marriage healthy, it will be important for me to become more _____ in our relationship.

(i.e., attentive, sensitive, respectful, accepting, appreciative)

I want to change in this way because I love you!

Here's a review for keeping your marriage healthy.

1. Your goal is intimacy. Give to your partner, so he/she is less alone in your marriage.

2. Remember to celebrate when good things happen. Don't leave your partner alone in their celebration.

3. Deeply know your partner's top relational needs and how they feel loved. Become aware of your own.

4. Learn to share your needs in a positive way.

5. Heal hurt you did not cause by giving comfort. Don't leave your partner alone in their hurt.

6. Heal hurt you have caused with a good apology. Choose to forgive. That heals anger.

7. Help each other with any unhealthy thinking.

8. Stay at the top of the Pain and Potential Chart. Meet your partner's needs.

Relational Needs Assessment

This exercise will enable you to better identify the priority of your relational needs.

Instructions:

Take time to individually respond to the following statements by placing the appropriate number beside each sentence. When you have completed all 50 statements, you may interpret your answers by using the *Identifying Your Top Needs Scoring*.

Strongly Disagree	Disagree	Neutral	Agree	Strongly Agree
1	2	3	4	5

Name: _____ Date: _____

___1.   It is important that people receive me for who I am—even if I'm a little "different."

___2.   It is important to me that my world is in order.

___3.   I sometimes grow tired of trying to do my best.

___4.   It is significant to me when others ask my opinion.

___5.   It is important that I receive frequent physical hugs, warm embraces, etc.

___6.   I feel good when someone takes a special interest in the things that are important to me.

___7.   It is important for me to know "where I stand" with those who are in authority over me.

___8.   It is meaningful when someone notices that I need help and then offers to get involved.

___9.   When I feel overwhelmed, I especially need someone to come alongside me and help.

___10. I feel pleased when someone recognizes and shows concern for how I'm feeling emotionally.

___11. I like to know that I am significant and valued by others.

___12. Generally speaking, I don't like a lot of solitude.

___13. I like it when my loved ones say to me, "I love you."

___14. I don't like being seen only as a part of a large group—my individuality is important.

___15. I am pleased when a friend calls to listen to me and encourage me.

___16. It is important to me that people acknowledge me not just for what I do but for who I am.

___17. I feel best when my world is orderly and somewhat predictable.

___18. When I've worked hard on a project, I am pleased to have people acknowledge my work and express gratitude.

___19. When I "blow it," it is important to me to be reassured that I am still loved.

___20. It is encouraging to me when I realize that others notice my skills and strengths.

___21. I sometimes feel overwhelmed and discouraged.

___22. It's important to me to be treated with kindness and equality, regardless of my race, gender, looks, and status.

_____23. To have someone I care about touch me on the arm or shoulder or give me a hug feels good.

_____24. I enjoy it when someone wants to spend time with just me.

_____25. It is meaningful when someone I look up to says, "Good job."

_____26. It is important to me for someone to show concern for me after I've had a hard day.

_____27. While I may feel confident about what I "do" (my talents, gifts, etc.), I also believe that I need other people's input and help.

_____28. Written notes and calls expressing sympathy after the death of a loved one, health problems, or other stressful events are (or would be) very meaningful to me.

_____29. I feel good when someone shows satisfaction with the way I am.

_____30. I enjoy being spoken well of or affirmed in front of a group of people.

_____31. I would be described as an "affectionate" person.

_____32. When a decision is going to affect my life, it is important to me that my input is sought and given serious consideration.

_____33. I am pleased when someone shows interest in current projects on which I am working.

_____34. I appreciate trophies, plaques, and special gifts, which are permanent reminders of something significant that I have done.

_____35. It is not unusual for me to worry about the future.

_____36. When I am introduced into a new environment, I typically search for a group of people with whom I can connect.

_____37. The possibility of major change (moving, new job, etc.) produces anxiety for me.

_____38. It bothers me when people are prejudiced against others just because they dress or act differently.

_____39. It is necessary for me to be surrounded by friends and loved ones who will be there through thick and thin.

_____40. Receiving written notes and expressions of gratitude particularly pleases me.

_____41. To know that someone is thinking of me is very meaningful.

_____42. People who try to control me or others annoy me.

_____43. I am pleased by unexpected and spontaneous expressions of care.

_____44. I feel important when someone looks me in the eye and listens to me without distractions.

_____45. I am grateful when people commend me for a positive characteristic I exhibit.

_____46. I don't like to be alone when experiencing hurt and trouble; it is important for me to have a companion who will be with me.

_____47. I don't enjoy working on a project by myself; I prefer to have a "partner" on important projects.

_____48. It is important for me to know I am part of the group.

_____49. I respond to someone who tries to understand me emotionally and who shows me caring concern.

_____50. When working on a project, I would rather work with a team of people than by myself.

Identifying Your Top Needs Scoring

Add up your responses corresponding to each question to find the totals related to each need.

Acceptance

1 _____
19 _____
36 _____
38 _____
48 _____
Total _____

Respect

4 _____
14 _____
22 _____
32 _____
42 _____
Total _____

Comfort

10 _____
26 _____
28 _____
46 _____
49 _____
Total _____

Security

2 _____
17 _____
35 _____
37 _____
39 _____
Total _____

Affection

5 _____
13 _____
23 _____
31 _____
43 _____
Total _____

Support

8 _____
9 _____
27 _____
47 _____
50 _____
Total _____

Appreciation

11 _____
18 _____
25 _____
34 _____
40 _____
Total _____

Attention

6 _____
12 _____
24 _____
30 _____
44 _____
Total _____

Encouragement

3 _____
15 _____
21 _____
33 _____
41 _____
Total _____

Approval

7 _____
16 _____
20 _____
29
45 _____
Total _____

1. What were your three highest totals? Which needs do they represent?

2. What were your three lowest totals? Which needs do they represent?

Marriage Intimacy Inventory

Strongly Disagree	Disagree	Neutral	Agree	Strongly Agree
1	2	3	4	5

1. My partner is supportive and encouraging in areas of personal belief and values.   1   2   3   4   5

2. We seem to be good at giving one another undivided attention when listening or talking.   1   2   3   4   5

3. My partner is attentive and sensitive to my needs in the area of sexual foreplay.   1   2   3   4   5

4. We seem to practice honest confession followed by genuine forgiveness when one of us has hurt the other.   1   2   3   4   5

5. When I'm sharing my feelings, my partner values them and is sensitive to provide understanding reassurance.   1   2   3   4   5

6. I'm comfortable communicating to my partner my sexual desires and preferences.   1   2   3   4   5

7. It would be characteristic for us to share together some of our long range dreams and hopes—even if they seem silly.   1   2   3   4   5

8. Sharing appreciation and verbalizing love are two things my partner is very good at.   1   2   3   4   5

9. We seem to prioritize frequent times of quality conversation and having dates together.   1   2   3   4   5

10. We seem to frequently recount the good times and blessings we have enjoyed.   1   2   3   4   5

11. I remember special times when my partner and I shared together in strong emotions, like grief, sadness, and joy.   1   2   3   4   5

12. I'm very satisfied with my partner's sensitivity in meeting my sexual needs.   1   2   3   4   5

13. In many of the important issues concerning values and beliefs, my partner and I often tend to agree.   1   2   3   4   5

14. Verbalizing to my partner my needs and desires concerning our relationship would be normal for me.   1   2   3   4   5

15. I am satisfied in my partner's frequency of initiating sexual times together.   1   2   3   4   5

Interpreting Your Score:

Your Spiritual Closeness: Personal beliefs and values

Add your responses for questions No. 1, 4, 7, 10, 13 and chart your score below:

0	5	10	15	20	25

Your Emotional Closeness: Friendship

Add your responses for questions No. 2, 5, 8, 11, 14 and chart your score below:

0	5	10	15	20	25

Your Physical Closeness: Physical intimacy

Add your responses for questions No. 3, 6, 9, 12, 15 and chart your score below:

0	5	10	15	20	25

Did any new insights or questions come to mind as you completed this inventory?

Couple Sharing Time

Share with each other three ways in which you would like to continue deepening your experience of intimacy. Be specific about how this action plan can be achieved and when each of the things you list will take place.

Intimacy Action Plan

Three ways I would like to deepen our relationship:

1. _____.

2. _____.

3. _____.

Three ways my **husband/wife** would like to deepen our relationship:

1. _____.

2. _____.

3. _____.

Our Intimacy Action Plan

Three ways we are planning together to deepen our experience of marriage intimacy:

What?

_____

_____

How?

_____

_____

When?

_____

_____

THE PAIN AND POTENTIAL OF RELATIONAL NEEDS

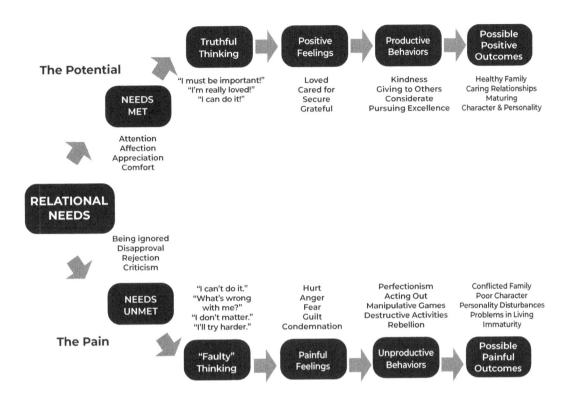

The Potential

Truthful Thinking → Positive Feelings → Productive Behaviors → Possible Positive Outcomes

"I must be important!"
"I'm really loved!"
"I can do it!"

Loved
Cared for
Secure
Grateful

Kindness
Giving to Others
Considerate
Pursuing Excellence

Healthy Family
Caring Relationships
Maturing
Character & Personality

NEEDS MET

Attention
Affection
Appreciation
Comfort

RELATIONAL NEEDS

Being ignored
Disapproval
Rejection
Criticism

NEEDS UNMET

"I can't do it."
"What's wrong with me?"
"I don't matter."
"I'll try harder."

Hurt
Anger
Fear
Guilt
Condemnation

Perfectionism
Acting Out
Manipulative Games
Destructive Activities
Rebellion

Conflicted Family
Poor Character
Personality Disturbances
Problems in Living
Immaturity

The Pain

"Faulty" Thinking → Painful Feelings → Unproductive Behaviors → Possible Painful Outcomes

Unhealthy Thinking Patterns

1. Polarizing

- **There is only one way to do something.**
- **Everything is right or wrong.**
- **The world is seen in absolutes.**

Description

Polarizing is a perfectionistic thinking pattern that views life as all or nothing, good or bad, right or wrong. This can be difficult to live with because the tendency is to be judgmental and exacting.

Polarizers judge their own and others' performance on the basis of their own impossible standards. When they don't attain their idea of perfection, they may suffer with great anger and despair. They tend to focus on what is wrong rather than what is right. Rigid rules are held for evaluating life. Little satisfaction is felt in modest performance even though there has been genuine effort. Even when successful, little joy is expressed because success was expected anyway.

Background

Legalistic, critical, or performance-orientated families can give rise to these perfectionist attitudes. In such homes, a child may have had many insecurities and fears. Perhaps whatever a child did was never good enough. Perhaps others around them were consistently criticized and evaluated. Homes that were extremely unstructured might also contribute to the development of this tendency.

Truth

The process of achieving something, including effort and motivation, also have value even when the end result is disappointing. Some issues are right or wrong, but many are shades of gray or nuanced. Middle ground may need to be defined for many issues, and multiple options to solve a problem may need to be identified.

Effects within a Marriage

Polarizers may tend to define every issue very simplistically. They have a pessimistic view of life and find difficulty enjoying fun times. They are easily discouraged and disillusioned. They can be rejecting and accusing of others with a tendency to attack, to become angry or resentful, and to withdraw.

Overcoming Polarizing

Be aware of your reactions and analyze what prompted your response. For example: One aspect of a project being worked on is criticized.

A **polarizing** reaction says, "This project is useless. I'm trashing it!" Anger is felt both towards the critic and personally.

If "This project is useless" is replaced with "The project wasn't perfect, but there was a lot of good in it. I can improve it," the response can be to evaluate the criticism, consider changes, and move on.

Dispute faulty thinking and practice new responses with your partner's help and support.

Replace Faulty Thinking	More Truthful Responses
Replace: *"If it's not done this way, it won't work."*	With: *"My way is not the only way; others' ways may work too."*
Replace:	With:
Replace:	With:

2. Personalizing

- **Life events are perceived as personal rejections and attacks.**

- **There is a "It must be my fault" thought pattern.**

Description

A **personalizer** tends to assume that most of life's events are directly related to themselves. This creates unnecessary stress when things that happen are seen as rejections or attacks. Someone who **personalizes** can be moody and easily hurt, blaming himself (or herself) for everything. Others may describe them as fragile or too sensitive. They are often insecure and tend towards self-condemnation.

Background

Personalizers often come from a highly critical or neglectful home environment where he/she was often wrongly blamed for whatever was happening. The child may have grown up with negative self talk, "What's wrong with me?"

Truth

We are not the target or cause of everything that happens to us. Usually, what occurs has nothing to do with us or is more a statement about the other person than about us.

Effects within a Marriage

When we take everything personally, we run the risk of overreacting to our spouse and causing unnecessary tensions in our marriage.

Overcoming Personalizing

Begin by taking notice of incidents when personalizing has taken place. Writing them may even be helpful. Strong feelings of anger, upset, or hurt may lie beneath the self-blaming. Ask for help.

For example: *A friend cancels coming for coffee because she needs to visit her mother in the hospital.*

A **personalizer's** reaction might be *"She probably didn't want to come for coffee anyway."* The consequences of that reaction are that feelings of rejection, hurt, and annoyance surface. Concern for the friend's mother is neglected. The thought process might develop into, *"She probably doesn't like me anyway. In fact, no one really likes me."* A more truthful reaction might be, *"I feel disappointed that our coffee date won't take place, but my friend must go care for her mother. I'll look forward to us being able to rearrange for another day. I wonder how I can support my friend while her mother is ill."*

Replace Faulty Thinking	More Truthful Responses
Replace: *"I'm sure it's my fault."*	With: *"I may have contributed to the problem, but I need more information before I accept total responsibility."*
Replace:	With:
Replace:	With:

3. Generalizing

- **Past experiences become predictors of the future.**

Description

Generalizing is exhibited when someone believes that past events will always predict the future. They tend to assume that whatever has happened before will unavoidably happen again. This is a deterministic view that doesn't discriminate sufficiently. It is a self-defeating thought pattern that prevents trust. This thought process can feed a cynical pessimistic outlook. The belief is that nothing will or even can change, including a person.

There is a gloomy attitude about the future. Such a thought process is associated with doubt, fear, and insecurity. Little initiative is shown and other people are easily written off.

Background

Training in this thinking pattern begins often in the home environment where it was modeled by one or both parents during the partner's childhood. It may result from past painful disappointments that were dealt with alone.

Truth

What has happened before does not have to happen again. Things can be different and even better though some effort may be required for that change to occur.

Effects within a Marriage

An attitude develops that says, *"No matter what we do, we'll never get along with each other."* **Generalizers** hold on to past hurts, failures, and rejections and use them as evidence for their gloomy attitude towards the future (i.e., one argument with a neighbor must mean we will never have anything more to do with them).

Overcoming Generalizing

Begin by recognizing how often you are giving this message and pinpoint specific examples.

For example: A **generalizer** eats something not allowed on a new diet then reacts: *"Dieting doesn't work."*

Consequences of the reaction: They stop trying, become self-condemning, and may eat even more unhealthily.

Replace with: *"I am in control of my eating, and I choose whether to eat or not."*

With more truthful thinking, the response to one failed day on a new diet will be: *"I'll begin again now."*

Replace Faulty Thinking	More Truthful Responses
Replace: *"I've never had good grades before so why bother? I'll never be a good student."*	With: *"My low grades before were probably the result of not studying well. I can learn how to study and, with effort, raise my grades."*
Replace:	With:
Replace:	With:

4. Magnifying

- Making a "big deal" out of "little things" may be exhibited.
- Making mountains out of molehills is common.

Description

Magnifying is the tendency to exaggerate events until everything seems like a catastrophe. This person may be volatile with anger, unmerciful with self-condemnation, or overwhelmed with fear or self pity. Others may view them as self-absorbed, preoccupied with their own crises, whiny, and over-reactive.

Background

The childhood home may have been an environment in which little things were blown out of proportion. Discipline may have been excessive and out of proportion to the offense. Spilled milk provoked a character attack. Perhaps a parent was preoccupied with their own situation (experiencing loneliness, rejection, or fear), which contributed to them seeing catastrophes in every situation. A parent may inappropriately have expected a child to take responsibility beyond their ability or maturity, resulting in the child feeling overwhelmed.

Possible Indicators of Magnifying

Frequent use of extreme words and phrases such as **never, every, devastated, worst, ruined, terrible, horrible, awful, beyond repair, too late, all, and nothing** are possible indicators. This exaggerated thinking may produce self–condemnation.

Truth

Molehills are not mountains. Not everything is a major event. A 50 cent event needs a 50 cent reaction. People sometimes treat us badly but not always. We do get some things wrong but not everything.

Effects within a Marriage

This environment can seem like every little event is made to feel like a catastrophe. When difficult events do arise, we have little ability to cope. Emotional energy is sapped by trying to exist through all the "big" events.

Overcoming Magnifying

Be alert for the trigger words: **always, every, no one, never, awful, worst, terrible, horrible**. Analyze what caused this sort of response then take your thoughts captive and replace them with more rational, truthful thinking.

For example: A coffee mug is dropped and breaks.

A **magnifier's** reaction: *"That's it. My whole day is ruined!"*

Consequences of that response: The **magnifier** might exhibit a negative attitude, which results in a bad day, anger, depression, and self blame.

Replace with a different thought process: *"These things happen; it's just a mug that can easily be replaced. I'll clean it up."*

Replace Faulty Thinking	More Truthful Responses
Replace: *"Everything is ruined!"*	With: *"This situation isn't so good, but I can get over it."*
Replace:	With:
Replace:	With:

5. Minimizing

- **Feelings associated with significant life events or issues are denied.**
- **Making a "little deal" out of emotional pain is a common response.**

Description

People who **minimize** will often say, "It really doesn't matter." When someone doesn't express or acknowledge their own emotions, they tend not to expect others to have feelings either. Even during life's major events, little emotion is shown or expected of others. Minimizers have trouble labeling or experiencing emotions other than anger. When pressed to communicate, they give facts, opinions, and reasons instead of vulnerably sharing their needs or feelings. Even when feeling significant hurt or anger, minimizers will often deny that anything is wrong or that anything troubles them. Much effort may be expended to "put a positive spin on things." Impatience can be shown towards those who more readily show emotion.

Background

Minimizers often come from homes where personal needs were neglected or overlooked. To cope with pain, they have learned to "shut down" and act as if nothing is wrong. Such a person may have been encouraged to deny their own needs, which promotes losing touch with their own feelings. They may have become self-reliant or self-sufficient, having seen this pattern modeled by those close to them.

Truth

Some of life's events are major happenings and are worth a significant emotional and/or behavioral response.

Effects within a Marriage

Minimizers often leave spouses feeling lonely, frustrated, and hurt particularly during tragic events when little or no feeling is demonstrated. They deny that anything troubles them and are also averse to acknowledging pain in others

Overcoming Minimizing

When someone has unmet needs, they may not recognize that showing emotion about painful experiences is healthy. They may be able to show their emotions after receiving comfort. They may need to be reassured that showing emotions is not the same as losing control. Trust of a spouse may allow a **minimizer** to begin verbalizing feelings. For a **minimizer**, to show emotion is often a sign of weakness but this can be identified as an unhelpful thinking pattern. The more positive response of recognizing and acknowledging feelings can be chosen.

For example: *A married couple is having problems in their marriage.*

A **minimizer's** reaction: *"What problems? My spouse thinks we have problems; I don't."* Consequences of that response: They may deny, demonstrate little or no feelings, or give facts, opinions, or data instead of sharing feelings.

Replace Faulty Thinking	More Truthful Responses
Replace: *"This happens to everyone; I'll get over it."*	With: *"As I feel my pain, grieve the hurt, and receive comfort, I'll get over it."*
Replace:	With:
Replace:	With:

6. Emotional Reasoning

- **Confusing feelings with facts is a common thought pattern.**

- **"If I feel it—it's true!"**

Description

This thinking pattern reflects the statement: "If I feel something it must be true." Someone who is an **emotional reasoner** puts feelings on the same level as facts. Feelings, thoughts, and facts are all confused, and truth becomes distorted.

A wife who can't feel a husband's care about a hurtful experience may unreasonably accuse her partner of not caring. A more precise statement might be "I don't think you care," or "I'm afraid that you don't care." In this latter statement, the real emotion—fear—is honestly expressed.

Background

Growing up experiences play a significant role in producing this distorted thinking pattern. Living with a parent who modeled **emotional reasoning** makes it difficult for a child to distinguish feelings from facts. Betrayal of one parent by another may have been witnessed. When broken promises are a frequent experience in childhood, an attitude which says, "I'll believe it when I see it," is prompted. Deep emotional trauma such as physical or sexual abuse in childhood may have been experienced. A child who frequently felt afraid but didn't receive any help dealing with their fears may grow into an adult who finds it hard to distinguish feelings from facts.

Truth

Even though "I feel it," it may not be true. Feelings are feelings, no more and no less. They are not facts. When I say, "I feel that..." I'm really expressing important emotions such as hurt, fear, or anger. I need to identify the real feelings and vulnerably express them.

Effects within a Marriage

Confusing feelings for facts can make problems in a marriage. Accusations that are based on emotion rather than evidence can permeate a relationship (i.e., "I feel jealous therefore my husband/ wife must be having an affair"). Such a home will be dominated by fear and mistrust. The partner often becomes very frustrated.

Overcoming Emotional Reasoning

Accept the truth that feelings have their place, but they can't take the place of truth. Notice incidents when **emotional reasoning** has been allowed to dominate. Allow your partner to talk about this with you. Identify unhelpful thought patterns and think about true responses.

For example: *How should one respond when a husband or wife comes home late from work?*

A reaction based on **emotional reasoning**: *"I just know he/she is with someone else."* Consequences of the reaction: The marriage partner may be accusing, attacking, angry, or resentful.

Replace with: *"There is probably a good reason for their delay."*

With more truthful thinking, the response to your partner when they return can be: *"I get very concerned when you are late and become fearful about the reason for your delay."*

Replace Faulty Thinking	More Truthful Responses
Replace: *"That's just how I feel."*	With: *"My feelings are important, but they may not be consistent with truth."*
Replace:	With:
Replace:	With:

Respond to Emotion with Emotion

Sometimes we find that we don't know how to put into words what is going on inside us, regardless of how much we might want to include our spouse in how we are feeling. A husband or wife, frustrated at their partner's lack of sharing, may criticize or blame without understanding that, to the one struggling with expressing their emotions, this kind of sharing seems almost impossible to do.

Distinguishing the numerous emotions we may be experiencing related to just one event can be helped by developing a greater vocabulary of feeling words. Looking over such a list of words can help us define and describe the complex emotions we are feeling.

30 Positive Emotions

Grateful	Happy	Hopeful	Joyful
Loved	Understood	Important	Relieved
Sympathetic	Successful	Amused	Determined
Kind	Creative	Satisfied	Delighted
Tender	Helpful	Enthusiastic	Mellow
Relaxed	Contented	Optimistic	Thoughtful
Confident	Ecstatic	Surprised	Impressed
Efficient	Encouraged		

30 Painful Emotions

Disappointed	Frightened	Nervous	Insecure
Rejected	Regretful	Mad	Embarrassed
Convicted	Disgusted	Resentful	Confused
Frustrated	Remorseful	Sorrowful	Jealous
Discouraged	Depressed	Scared	Sad
Lonely	Hopeless	Afraid	Ashamed
Anxious	Worried	Apologetic	Bitter
Enraged	Worthless		

As words are sought to describe emotions and feelings, it may be necessary to look at these lists many times before sharing becomes more comfortable and spontaneous.

Deepening Intimacy as Lovers

Sexual intimacy is for our pleasure and delight. Sometimes, however, we have known disappointment about our sexual times together. Sexual intimacy may be an area of frustration and a current painful issue for some couples. Anxiety, fear, anger, or resentment may be associated with the sexual relationship. The target of deep, mutual satisfaction sexually may feel like an unobtainable goal.

Talking about sexual needs can often be difficult, but being open with one another becomes more possible when we change how we talk about our sexual relationship.

If sex is viewed as **something we do,** it may easily be evaluated like other activities (i.e., How often? What is the performance like?).

If sex is viewed as **something we have,** it may become something we manage or conditionally agree to (i.e., once the decorating is finished or if you are home on time all week). Conflicts may follow manipulations, bargaining, or spouses who disengage from sexual intimacy!

In constrast, it's more helpful to talk about sex as **something that you share**! Sexual intimacy is all about having the freedom to give **all** of yourself to your husband/wife. When we give to each other, each partner feels cherished and valued.

Cultivating Romance

Anticipating a sexually intimate time together can increase romance. For instance, you might part in the morning with words that express the desire to be together at the end of the day. Focus on giving, not taking: *"How can I increase your enjoyment tonight?"*

Remember to give to each other emotionally for the most passionate love-making. Share feelings, heal hurts, praise character qualities, and ask about each other's day. Increase non-sexual touching.

The exercise known as a Love Map provides opportunity to talk to each other about sexual times together. It is an effective tool to discuss what sexual intimacy looks like to you both! (i.e., It would not be unusual for a wife's Love Map to mention days prior to the sexually intimate time.)

For example: As a precursor to Saturday night, come home on time on Wednesday. Have a meal together on Thursday and talk together. Go out together on Saturday evening before we have sex.

This should not be confused with manipulating or bargaining. The time spent together on the evenings before Saturday night are giving to the wife's emotional needs and preparing her to be able to give freely to her husband.

As you complete the following Love Map, remember that your partnership is unique and enjoy the freedom that thought gives.

SCAN ME

Scan this
QR code to
download
the Love Map
exercise sheet.

Love Map

Hindrances to sexual intimacy

Four of the major hindrances to sexual intimacy are addressed in this exercise.

1. **Lack of openness/communication:** Sex is not an easy subject to discuss for some couples; avoidance of the topic leaves many couples in a cycle of little openness, resentments, and frustrations.

2. **Unhealthy preoccupation with getting rather than giving:** Tragically, many of us grew up with a mindset that sex was something to be taken, earned, or manipulated; the art of giving oneself to another person is foreign to us and awkward.

3. **Boredom:** Lack of creativity and freshness or sameness produce complacency and feelings of obligation and duty, while creativity communicates initiative, desire, and anticipation.

4. **Lack of anticipation and expectancy:** Your mind is your most important sexual resource. Learning to mentally anticipate times of being together with your spouse builds excitement, creativity, and desire.

Each spouse answers the following:

"From my point of view, an ideal sexually intimate time with my spouse would include the following."

Include personally meaningful items related to timing, location, clothing, and romantic preparations. You might want to consider personal preferences related to initiative, foreplay, positions, and "after–play."

1. _____
2. _____
3. _____
4. _____
5. _____
6. _____

7. _____
8. _____
9. _____
10. _____
11. _____
12. _____

Pick a private time and place to exchange your Love Maps.

When you exchange them, discuss as much as you are comfortable discussing. Clarify and answer questions as appropriate. You will grow more comfortable with doing this as you repeat the exercise.

Plan ahead for two times of sexual intimacy to fulfill both love maps. Each person should give their spouse freedom to fulfill as much of the Love Map as he/she is now comfortable with. It is important not to insist or push your partner.

Marriage intimacy is the freedom to share all of one's self with another person—body, soul, and spirit. Fulfilling the Love Map is part of expressing that freedom through giving to and receiving from one another.

For example: A husband gives first to his wife by fulfilling her Love Map. A wife will then choose another time to give to her husband and fulfill his Love Map.

Plan these times so that both spouses anticipate the intimacy throughout the day. Spend moments anticipating the pleasures of becoming one physically.

Freely share all of yourself with one another. Preparing, discussing, and fulfilling a Love Map can become a regular part of intimacy along with other spontaneous times of coming together sexually.

Intimacy as a way of life

To transform our marriages into the wonderful relationships they were designed to be, we need to practice the disciplines and skills that this course has introduced.

Our desire is that you are already experiencing greater oneness in each of the three dimensions—emotionally, spiritually, and physically. It may be helpful to look again at the assessment you completed for each of these areas in Session One.

Throughout your married lives, let it be your goal to increase intimacy in each area.

Your answers to the set of questions on the **Marriage Intimacy Inventory** *(pages 40-42)*, will provide you with further clarification and the opportunity to share how intimacy can be increased in the coming days, weeks, months, and years.

Marriage Team Meeting

Marriage Team Meetings are specific times to talk about any calendar coordination, planning, goal evaluation, or expressions of closeness that will keep your marriage healthy.

- Make time to put Marriage Team Meetings into your calendars. If you have been meeting for this course one evening a week, you might continue to preserve this same evening for your Marriage Team Meetings. Remember that sharing fun times is also important; you may also want to plan ahead for some date nights.

Here are some ideas that could be a part of your Marriage Team Meetings. Some ideas will require more than one meeting:

- Referring to the two lists of emotional words on page 52, take turns identifying some of the feelings each of you is experiencing. These could be related to work, family, church, or marriage. Developing a vocabulary of positive words is as important as being able to describe painful emotions. You may want to reflect that in your sharing.

- Using the list of character qualities on pages 34–36, choose three that describe your husband or wife and share them. Remember to identify specific times when this quality has been demonstrated.

- Complete this sentence: *"Three important things I especially want to remember and practice from Keeping Marriages Healthy are..."*

"Which three things would you especially like me to remember and practice from Keeping Marriages Healthy?" Write these three here:

1. _____

2. _____

3. _____

Continue to work on your future plans for increasing marriage intimacy. You may find it helpful to jot down the initial items you want to begin devoting time to and plan when you might take action. Select one of these to begin working on in this meeting.

- Exchange your Love Maps and make plans to fulfill them both.

Establishing Marriage Team Meetings

How much time? A typical recommendation would be to set aside an hour to an hour and a half each week to talk together.

Schedule a time: Don't leave it to chance! Lunch on Thursday, Tuesday evening after the children are in bed, or even a Saturday morning breakfast are possible times.

If the time has to change each week, arrange the time routinely (i.e., Sunday evening).

Prioritize the time: Make it inviolate as much as possible. The consistency each week is important, but the emotional benefit of prioritizing one another in this time encourages closeness.

Protect the time: To limit interruptions and distractions, find a quiet place at home or outside without phones or visitors.

Marriage Team Meetings: Possible Agenda Items

A fearful thought for many couples would be: "What in the world would we talk about?"

1. Coordinate calendars for the coming week.

- What is planned? What are the children doing, and what needs do they have? Who is working late?

- What social activities are planned? Operate from a principle of agreeing together on time commitments which affect the family before saying, "yes."

- Plan your next time of going out together as a couple and your next family outing.

2. Discuss family goals, monitoring progress and working together.

- Written annual goals might be developed for the family and broken down into weekly or monthly target dates.

- Do the finances look tight this week? How can we help?

- What is our next. planned household expenditure, and how could each of us better contribute to achieve it?

- Do we have any new friends that we want to spend time getting to know better this year?

- How are our personal goals progressing—reading, diet, exercise, hobbies—and how can we encourage/support one another?

3. Parenting Plans: It is better to plan and become united than have the children divide and rule. Discuss significant discipline issues. What seems to be working, and what isn't?

- Plan family times together, plus individual times for each child.
- Discuss and agree upon parenting responsibilities for the next week or more (i.e., Who is needing help? Who is needing a break?).
- In this season of life, what goals seem reasonable for our children in terms of behavior, attitude, and responsibilities? How can we work together to achieve them?

4. Listening Times: One or the other spouse may just need to talk.

- Share stresses at work or with friendships.
- Share hopes and dreams.
- Share feelings and insights about recent moodiness.
- Share concerns and fears about "us," the children, finances, the future.
- You can't argue when one of you is listening. Give undivided attention, empathy, support, and eye contact.

5. Productive Expression of Needs: Lovingly share hopes for the future.

- Avoid "you" statements and generalities such as, *"You never spend any time with me"* or *"You always take the children's side against me!"*
- Use "I" and "we" statements positively.

  Examples: *"I really miss being alone together and hope we can plan to go out together soon."*

  "It would mean a lot to me if we could stay in agreement in front of the children and discuss any differences privately."

6. Appreciation: Express approval for who your partner is as well as appreciation for what he/she has done.

- Use your weekly meeting as a reminder that your husband/wife is a blessing to you! They do have good qualities!

  Examples: *"Thank you for the extra help you've given this week with the children."*

  "The way you greet me when I get in from work means a lot to me. You're so generous with affection and I love it!"

Confession, Forgiveness, and Comfort after Marriage Hurt

In every marriage, conflict, difficulty, and pain are inevitable. In even the best of marriages, both husbands and wives make mistakes, forget things, overlook needs, get too busy, or even take each other for granted. There really is no such thing as a perfect marriage. Why? Because, it is a relationship between two imperfect people.

The difficulties may be loud and angry, or they may be quiet and even somewhat hidden, but the question is not: "Do we hurt each other?" Rather, the question is: "When, how, and how much do we hurt each other, and what do we do about it?"

Identifying the hurt is the first part in the process of emptying an emotional cup filled with negative feelings of hurt, anger, fear and guilt. If we can empty these painful emotions, many of our symptoms will be addressed.

- **Comfort heals hurt.**
- **Guilt is emptied through confession.**
- **Anger and bitterness are resolved through forgiveness.**

Accepting responsibility

Many of us find focusing on someone else's faults is easier than focusing on our own.

Listing hurts done *to* us is often a lot easier than listing ways in which we have hurt our partner. Even when we have clearly done wrong (and it resulted in pain for our partner), we can resist taking responsibility for the action and try to justify or rationalize what occurred. This response will not bring healing.

In order for forgiveness and healing to occur, each partner must come to *realize and feel the other's pain.*

Confession of Hurts

(We suggest writing on a separate piece of paper rather than the workbook.)

1. Choose one of the main ways you have been a part of hurting your spouse. See page 62 for possibilities.

I hurt my husband/wife by...

Try to view this hurt from your husband's/wife's perspective.

Don't excuse yourself, avoid responsibility, or blame your husband/wife.

2. **When I hurt my husband/wife in this way, he/she probably felt...**

(i.e., sad, upset, discouraged, lonely, unappreciated, disrespected, invisible, unimportant, afraid, wounded, put down, ashamed, abandoned, used).

3. **Your husband/wife is in pain. Do you care?**

What feelings do you have for your spouse as you consider how you contributed to his/her pain (i.e., sad, regretful, remorse, pain, sorrowful, upset, deeply concerned)?

Feeling something (compassion, sorrow, etc.) for your spouse is important. You may be feeling guilty, ashamed, or angry, but these are feelings for or about you.

4. **Admit to the action/inaction. What I did was wrong—period. I hurt the other person.**

I need to be forgiven by my spouse.

5. **Express to your spouse your feelings of sorrow for the hurt you have caused and admit you're wrong without explanation or defensiveness.**

Using words such as *"I really care about you and your feelings, and it saddens me that I've hurt you"* will help bring about healing. Confessing with clear words like, *"It was wrong of me to..." (i.e., lose my temper, not return your call, forget your birthday).*

6. **As you finish confessing and sharing, end your confession with a request for forgiveness.**

Ask your partner directly, *"Will you forgive me?"* This question demonstrates a great deal of vulnerability and humility. The question also provides the listening partner with the opportunity to choose to forgive.

Forgiveness

When we have been hurt, we must be careful not to let any angry feelings we have turn to bitterness, resentment, or retaliation. Forgiveness helps the offending partner, but ultimately, the one who has been hurt benefits by being freed from those negative emotions.

1. **Reflect on what pain you felt as you respond to your partner's request for forgiveness.**

I was hurt when...

_____

_____

_____

_____

2. Which need was unmet relative to that hurt?

What I really needed was...

3. Choose to forgive.

Forgiveness is a choice not a feeling. Even though you choose to forgive, you may not feel like doing so. Forgiveness means, *"to turn it loose, to let it go"*. It is the anger that you are deciding to let go. Sometimes before you are ready to do that, further opportunity is needed for your partner to understand the depth of your pain. Forgiveness has to be unconditional. Offering to forgive only if the promise is made not to do something again is not offering unconditional forgiveness. This kind of forgiveness is fear-based and is not productive.

4. When you make the choice to forgive, reach over and touch your spouse and verbalize your forgiveness by actually saying, *"I forgive you."*

Your partner needs to hear the words to help them receive your forgiveness, just as you need to say them in order to seal your decision to forgive.

Each entry on the confession list will need to be confessed and forgiven.

5. Deal with additional hurts.

Both may now want to ask: *"Are there any major hurts I've not seen that need my apology? Please share them with me, so I can confess them now and seek your forgiveness."*

6. After each partner gives and receives forgiveness, destroy the lists.

A Good Habit

Confession to others about the hurt we have caused, along with forgiveness of others who have hurt us, must become a daily habit. Otherwise, our emotional cup begins to fill again with hurtful emotions.

Sometimes, even though we have genuinely forgiven the offender, we may still feel the pain of a wrong done to us. Our response to that pain may be to assume inappropriate or false responsibility for not being forgiving enough and to feel guilty. What we actually need to ease that pain and empty the hurt from our cup is comfort.

Confession, forgiveness, and comfort are all vital ingredients for a healthy marriage.

Possible Ways I May Have Hurt My Spouse

There are times when we can all benefit from a list that helps prompt our needed apology. Review the list below in private. Let it be a reminder of possible ways you may have hurt your spouse. Each item you identify with will need your apology. As you make your confession, be sure to use the script and process provided on pages 20 and 59-61.

At times, have I been...

Insensitive?

Disrespectful?

Dismissive?

Angry?

Harsh?

Critical?

Selfish?

Demanding?

Rude?

Embarrassing?

Judgmental?

Sarcastic?

Mean-spirited?

Neglectful?

Cold?

Blaming?

Avoidant?

Passive-aggressive?

Condescending?

Negative?

Emotionally closed-off?

At times, have I...

...prioritized other people or other things as more important than my partner?

...focused more on what's wrong with my partner than what's right?

...taken teasing too far and it hurt my partner?

...left my spouse feeling alone or unimportant?

...been neglectful of my partner's relational needs and they felt hurt?

This COMEDY DATE NIGHT is an opportunity to enjoy a fun date with your partner. Jason Earls has a way of making people laugh by connecting us with real-life marriage and family situations.

These DATE NIGHT MENUS are a great way to have some meaningful conversation with your partner. Feel free to download one or all of the menus as each one is geared towards each of the relational needs.

COMEDY DATE NIGHT

Scan QR code above to watch a Comedy Date Night with comedian Jason Earls.

DATE NIGHT MENU

Scan QR code above to access FREE menus to use on a date night.

Keeping Marriages Healthy is available **in English and Spanish.**
These can be purchased at www.relationshippress.com.

These are faith-based resources that we offer to help continue to deepen the intimacy in your marriage. These can be purchased at www.relationshippress.com.

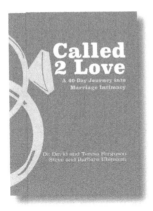

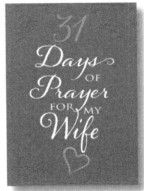

About the Relational Values Alliance

The Relational Values Alliance is a global alliance empowering people to experience and reproduce great relationships. We offer a variety of resources and workshops to help every dimension of your relationships flourish. We are committed to offering resources to help relationships:

- At home

Marriage resources are meant to help you and your significant other connect in a new way. Choose from date night options, growth plans, or articles to help strengthen your relationship.

Family resources are created to help you flourish with your children. Download our table talks for the whole family or read our collection of parenting blogs to get tips on how to start facilitating connection.

- At school

Our rapidly changing world has challenged the "why" behind learning and often leaves students with a longing to be a part of a greater cause or purpose. Our goal is to offer students an opportunity to discover more of their passion and learn to live it out.

- At work

RVA's customized materials and relational training are centered around: Growing Self, Growing Others, Growing Business, and Growing Legacy.

With more than 20 years of proven effectiveness, companies who have embraced a *Business as Unusual* lifestyle have experienced cultural change and increased profitability.

- In community

Caring communities are fundamental to a civil society and can serve as an avenue for transformation within its people. Community transformation is possible through relational enrichment. Research tells us, "We are each hardwired to connect, and without caring connection, bad things tend to happen."

- In faith

We strive to offer resources that can apply to all denominations and cultures with our partner, The Great Commandment Network.

For more information on how you, your home, school, church, community, or place of business can be served by Relational Values Alliance write or call:

Relational Values Alliance
2511 South Lakeline Blvd.
Cedar Park, Texas 78613
512.354.1464
Visit our website: relationalvalues.com or email: info@relationalvalues.com

- **Practical help to make good marriages better!**
- **Timely preparation for an upcoming marriage!**
- **Hope and healing for troubled relationships!**

International speakers and authors, David and Teresa Ferguson, offer tried-and-tested principles for discovering the secrets of a really great marriage. Experience a simple but profound way of relating to your partner that can lead to enjoying marriage for a lifetime!

This timely book will help you:

- Identify key relational needs and principles in order to better express your love.

- Discover secrets of healing hurts, building trust, and deepening communication.

- Gain the tools for resolving the inevitable conflict that arises in every marriage.

- Experience ways to have an intimate marriage—spiritually, emotionally, and physically.

Made in the USA
Middletown, DE
04 October 2021